Disney · PIXAR

Cars

ADVANCE
PUBLISHERS

Lightning McQueen was a rookie race car with big dreams. He wanted to be the next Piston Cup winner. But he had some fierce competition. There was Chick Hicks, a cruel competitor who bumped and crashed his way to each finish line. And there was The King, a fan favorite and nine-time Piston Cup winner.

At the racetrack, the green flag dropped, and the cars sped around the track.

Chick angrily slammed into Lightning, who skidded off the track. Then Chick crashed into another car on purpose. It caused a huge pileup, which was exactly what Chick wanted. He figured Lightning would never be able to get through the wreckage of cars.

Boy was he wrong! Lightning expertly dodged and weaved through the cars.

"What a spectacular move by Lightning McQueen!" the announcer exclaimed.

Lightning McQueen has a special way of avoiding a pileup during the Dinoco 400 —he even manages to wink at his adoring fans as he leaps by.

Ka-chow!!!

After a few more laps, Lightning drove in for a pit stop. But he refused to get his tires changed. With one lap to go, he had a huge lead when BANG! BANG! He blew his two rear tires.

As Lightning dragged himself toward the finish line, Chick and The King caught up. All three cars crossed the finish line at the same time. It was a three-way tie!

It was decided by racing officials that there would be a tie-breaker race in California.

Lightning McQueen was feeling overly confident at the start of the Piston Cup race, but to everyone's surprise, the race ended in a three-way tie!

The cars had one week to get to California. On the way, Lightning got separated from his trailer. He was terrified—and completely lost. He tried to get back to the interstate, but ended up on Highway 66 instead.

Suddenly, Lightning heard a siren behind him. An old police cruiser was on his tail. Lightning mistook the cruiser's backfires as gunshots and swerved into the little town of Radiator Springs. Panicking, he crashed into everything in sight. He ended up destroying the main street.

"Boy, you're in a heap of trouble," Sheriff told him.

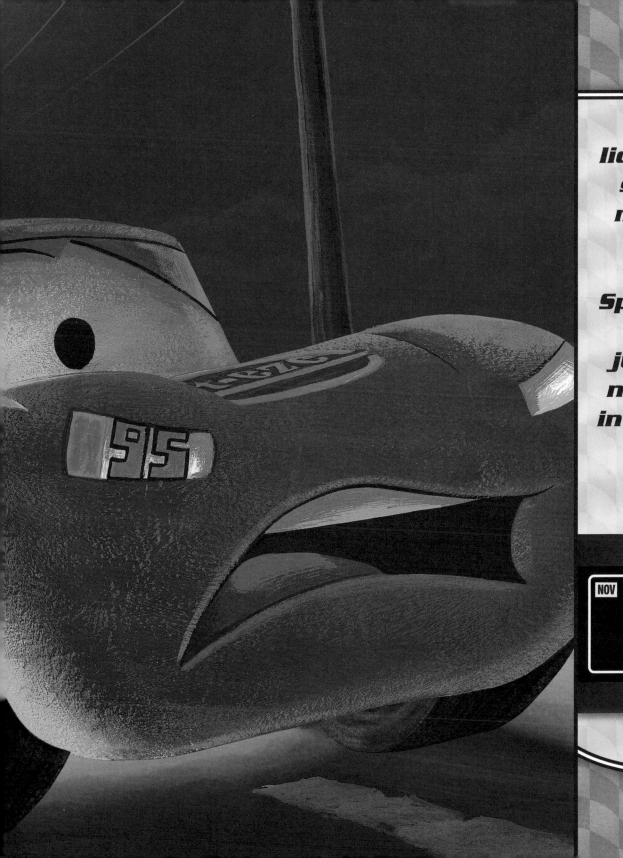

Sheriff's license plate shows his month and year, the Radiator Springs logo, and also just who is number one in Carburetor County!

NOV • CARBURETOR • 49
RS 001
COUNTY

The following morning, Lightning woke up in the impound lot. He was then towed into court by a rusty old tow truck named Mater.

The residents of Radiator Springs were inside the courtroom, furious that the red race car had torn up their town. Lightning was surprised that none of them knew who he was.

Doc Hudson was the judge, and he told Lightning he had to repair the road. Lightning couldn't believe it. He didn't have time for roadwork. He had to get to California for the race!

Doc Hudson, runs the local medical clinic and serves as the town judge. He looks after the health of every car in Radiator Springs.

Lightning was strapped to a huge road-paving machine named Bessie. Determined to get out of there as fast as possible, Lightning worked really quickly—and really poorly. When he was done, the road looked terrible!

Doc was very angry. "The deal was you fix the road, not make it worse. Now scrape it off and start over again."

"Hey, look Grandpa, I'm not a bulldozer," said Lightning. I'm a race car."

"Then why don't we have a little race, me and you?" Doc suggested. "If you win, you go, and I fix the road. If I win, you do the road my way."

Lightning thought it would be the easiest win in his racing career.

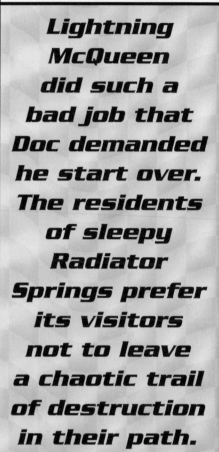

The town gathered at Willy's Butte to watch the big challenge. When the flag dropped, Lightning sped off. When the dust cleared, Doc was still at the starting line. He didn't look worried. Instead, he asked Mater to join him for a stroll.

Meanwhile, Lightning had raced down the dirt straightaway. As he approached a turn, he slid out. He rolled off a cliff and landed in a patch of cactus. Ouch!

Up above, Doc yelled down to Lightning, "You drive like you fix roads . . . lousy!" He left Mater to tow up the race car.

When they got back to town, Lightning honored the deal he had made and got busy fixing the road.

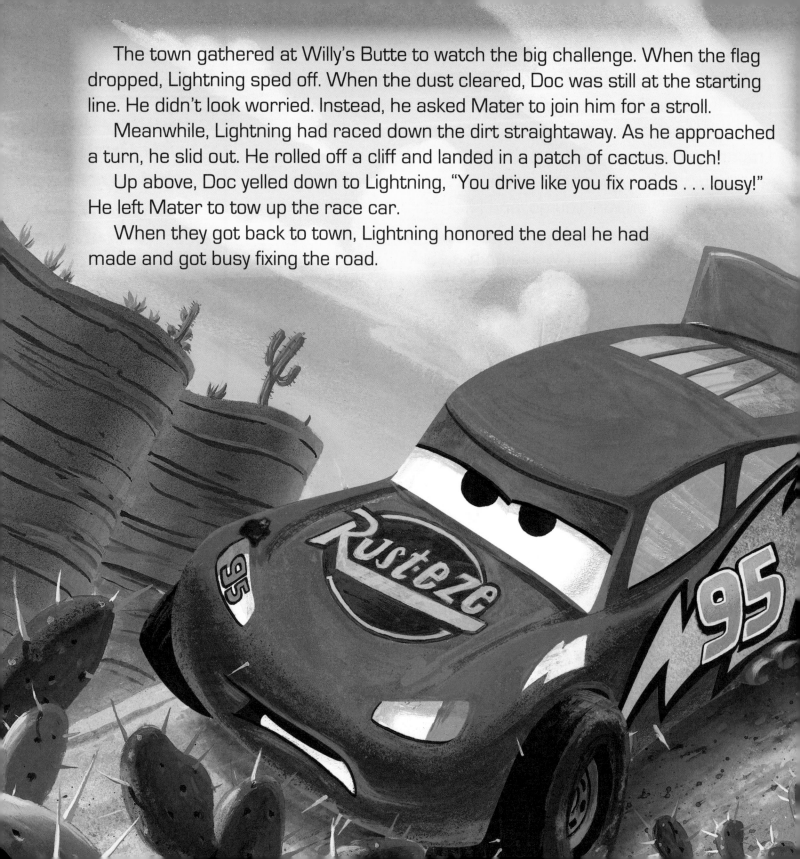

Mater's favorite leisure activity is tow-hook fishing, where he uses his hook to "fish" objects out of otherwise unreachable places.

The next morning, Lightning made a surprising discovery. He had accidentally wandered into Doc's back office and saw three Piston Cups. Doc was once the most famous race car around!

"You're the Hudson Hornet!" exclaimed Lightning. "How could you quit at the top of your game?"

"You think I quit? They quit on me," Doc said angrily. He showed Lightning a newspaper article about a wreck he had been in. When he got all fixed up and returned to racing, they told him a rookie had replaced him.

Although he never talks about his racing days, Doc still likes to take a spin around Willy's Butte when he thinks no one is looking.

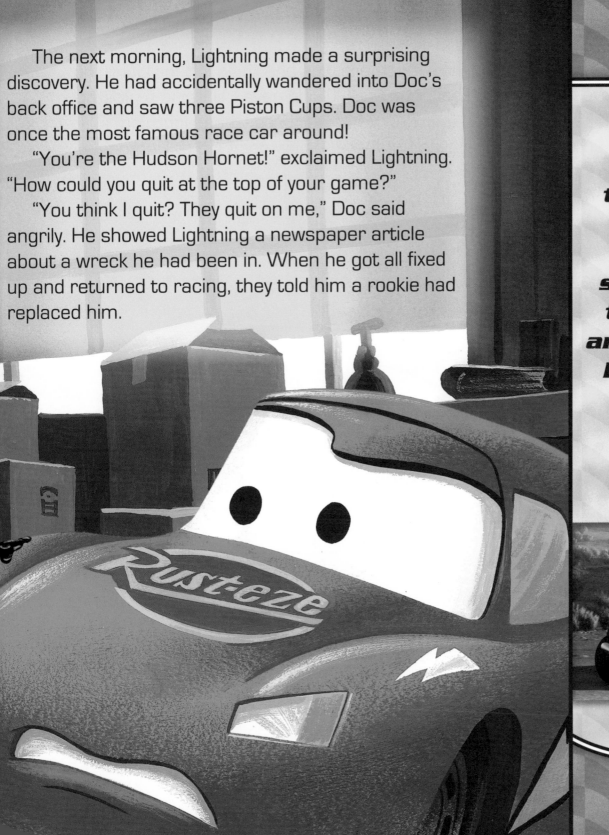

When the road was finally finished, there was one thing left for Lightning to do. He drove into Luigi's Casa Della Tires. Guido gave Lightning a pit stop overhaul, and Luigi suggested four new whitewall tires. Then Lightning visited every shop in town. He even got a brand-new paint job at Ramone's Body Shop.

Lightning McQueen helped everyone in town and became the best customer Radiator Springs had seen in a very long time.

While Lightning was in Radiator Springs, he realized that there was more to life than just racing. Friendship and teamwork were important, too.

Before he left for the race in California, there was time for one last cruise with his new friends.

Lightning finally made it to California and arrived at the Los Angeles International Speedway.

When the Piston Cup Championship was under way, Lightning tried to concentrate, but he kept thinking of his new friends back in Radiator Springs. He trailed Chick and The King by a full lap. It seemed that winning wasn't so important to him.

Suddenly, Doc's voice came over the radio! Doc had come to California to be Lightning's crew chief. In fact, many of Lightning's Radiator Springs friends had come to the race to be his pit crew!

Lightning zoomed back out onto the track. Now he was ready to win.

Before long, Lightning was in the lead. That's when Chick smashed into The King. The blue car spun into a wall and flipped over and over.

Just as Lightning approached the finish line, he glanced at the giant TV screen and saw what had happened to The King. It reminded him of what had happened to Doc. He couldn't let it happen to another great race car. Lightning slammed on his brakes.

While Chick passed him to cross the finish line and win the race, Lightning drove over to The King. Lightning pulled behind the battered car and began pushing The King over the finish line. The crowd cheered wildly. Even though he didn't win, Lightning was the hero of the day.

RIDDLES JOKES SILLY STUFF

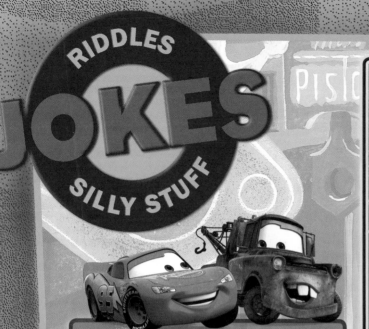

When is a car not a car?
When it turns into a garage

What would the U.S. be called if everyone in it drove pink cars?
A pink car-nation!

Why did Mater throw butter out his window?
He wanted to see a butterfly!

What did the nut say to the screw?
"Let's bolt."

What did the baby headlight say to the mommy headlight?
"I love you watts and watts!"

Why can't the motorcycle stand up on its own?
Because it is two tired.

What cop always sleeps under a blanket?
An undercover cop.

What is racecar spelled backwards?
Racecar!

What are Lightning McQueen's favorite critters?
Lightning bugs

What does Fillmore have in common with an elephant?
They both have the trunk in the front.

Knock, knock
Who's there?
Boo
Boo who?
Boo who . . .
I'm crying because Lightning's going to leave

Will you remember me tomorrow?
Yes.
Will you remember me next week?
Yes.
Will you remember me next month?
Yes.
Will you remember me next year?
Yes.
Knock, knock
Who's there?
You said you would remember me!

Knock, knock
Who's there?
Ya
Ya who?
Ya-who! Doc Hudson helped Lightning win the race.

Knock, knock
Who's there?
Ken
Ken who?
Ken you fix the road?

Knock, knock
Who's there?
Ketchup
Ketchup who?
Ketchup with you later.

Knock, knock
Who's there?
Les
Les who?
Les go back to Radiator Springs.

Knock, knock
Who's there?
Luke
Luke who?
Luke out that car's coming right toward you.

Knock, knock
Who's there?
Wendell
Wendell who?
Wendell we think Lightning will leave

How many words can you make from
HUDSON HORNET?

Unscramble: What is the name of the big race that Lightning wants to win? **TOSNIP CPU**

Circle every 3rd letter to find out what county Radiator Springs is in:
C _ _ _ _ _ _ _ _ COUNTY

FRAJYRMTBASUPORADECVTGAOBHR